# It's Elementary!

## 275 Math Word Problems

## Book 1

## M. J. Owen

Educators Publishing Service, Inc.
Cambridge and Toronto

*This book is dedicated to Joy Saco, my fifth-grade teacher,
for inspiring me to teach.*

Design by Joyce C. Weston
Illustrations by Tatjana Mai-Wyss

Printed in the U.S.A.
ISBN 0-8388-2411-0                    October 2000 Printing

# Contents

**7**    Addition

**37**    Subtraction

**66**    Addition and Subtraction Mixed Practice

**76**    Multiplication

**105**    Division

**136**    Multiplication and Division Mixed Practice

**147**    Final Mixed Review

# To the Teacher

Many elementary school students find math word problems to be challenging. In my own classroom, I have found that children often attempt to solve word problems too quickly. They fail to visualize the problem, and they do not identify key words. As a result, students try to solve a word problem using the wrong operation; for example, they may use division instead of multiplication.

The problem-solving approach that I teach my students is called TINS. The letters in this acronym stand for the different steps students use to analyze and solve word problems. While reading a word problem, students circle key words and note their THOUGHT (T) about the operation they should use to solve the problem. Next they circle and write down the important INFORMATION (I) from the word problem. At this stage I also encourage students to draw a picture of the information and to cross out information that doesn't seem important to the problem. Students then write their information as a NUMBER SENTENCE (N) and plug their answer into a SOLUTION SENTENCE (S). Here's an example:

Jodi has 7 books about cats and 8 books about birds. She visits a bookstore and buys 2 more books about cats. How many books about cats does Jodi have in all?

Thought: _____ + _____

Information: ____ 7 cat books, 2 more ____

____ cat books ____

Number Sentence: _____ 7 + 2 = ____

Solution Sentence: ____ Jodi has 9 books ____

____ about cats in all.

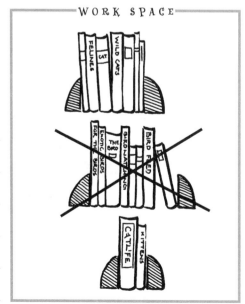

WORK SPACE

I hope this book—which covers addition, subtraction, multiplication, and division—will provide opportunities for fun and success with word problems. Happy problem solving!

# Solving Addition Word Problems with TINS

When you are reading a word problem, think of yourself as a detective. Key words can give you clues about how to solve each problem. Here are some addition key words:

- 🗝 in all
- 🗝 sum
- 🗝 add (and added)
- 🗝 altogether
- 🗝 total

You may want to add other addition words you know to this list.

When you see an addition key word in a problem, circle it and write **+** above the key word. Then write **+** on the THOUGHT line. Next circle and write down the important INFORMATION from the word problem. Sometimes it helps to draw a picture of the important information. It's also a good idea to cross out information that doesn't seem important to the problem. Now write your information as a NUMBER SENTENCE. Then plug your answer into your SOLUTION SENTENCE.

Check out this example problem:

Terrell has (6 toy trucks.) His mom takes him to the store and lets him pick out (2 more trucks) and 1 ~~toy car~~. How many (trucks) does Terrell have (in all?)

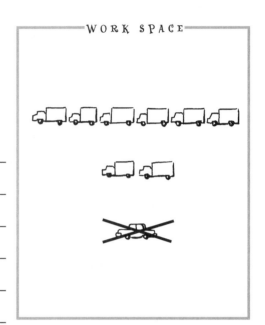

WORK SPACE

Thought: _____ + _____

Information: ___6 trucks, 2 more trucks___

_____

Number Sentence: ___6 + 2 =_____

Solution Sentence: ___Terrell has 8 toy___
___trucks in all._____

---

A good way to remember how to solve word problems is to think of the word *TINS*.

**T** = Thought
**I** = Information
**N** = Number Sentence
**S** = Solution Sentence

Good luck with problem solving!

Remember to check your work.

# Try It Out

Use TINS to solve these word problems. Remember to circle key words, draw pictures, and cross out extra information. The first 5 problems have pictures to help you.

**1.** Marcy went to the library and checked out 5 books. Her brother checked out 1 book. How many books did Marcy and her brother check out altogether?

WORK SPACE

Thought: _____

Information: _____

_____

Number Sentence: _____

Solution Sentence: _____

_____

**2.** Mrs. Cavazos has 3 hamsters. The fourth-grade teacher gives her 4 more hamsters to take care of over spring break. What is the total number of hamsters Mrs. Cavazos has now?

WORK SPACE

Thought: _____

Information: _____

_____

Number Sentence: _____

Solution Sentence: _____

_____

**3.** Gregory lost his pencil box. It contained 3 erasers, 10 pencils, and 7 pens. How many pencils and pens did Gregory lose in all?

Thought: _____

Information: _____

_____

Number Sentence: _____

Solution Sentence: _____

_____

WORK SPACE

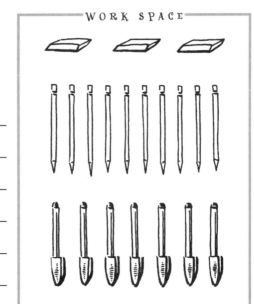

**4.** LaVotney went shopping. She bought 2 shirts, 1 pair of pants, and 3 sweaters. How many shirts and sweaters did LaVotney buy altogether?

Thought: _____

Information: _____

_____

Number Sentence: _____

Solution Sentence: _____

_____

WORK SPACE

**5.** Leanne invited 5 friends from her class to her birthday party. Later she invited 3 friends from her Girl Scout troop to the party. How many friends did Leanne invite in all?

Thought: _____

Information: _____

_____

Number Sentence: _____

Solution Sentence: _____

_____

WORK SPACE

**6.** At the fair Marty's family won 5 goldfish, 4 balloons, and 3 stuffed animals. How many goldfish and balloons did Marty's family win altogether?

Thought: _____

Information: _____

_____

Number Sentence: _____

Solution Sentence: _____

_____

WORK SPACE

**12**

**7.** The weather reporter said it snowed 2 inches on Monday, 3 inches on Tuesday, and 0 inches on Wednesday. What was the total amount of snowfall for the 3 days?

Thought: _____

Information: _____

_____

Number Sentence: _____

Solution Sentence: _____

_____

**8.** The track team at Baty Elementary ran 4 miles on Tuesday, 2 miles on Wednesday, and 3 miles on Thursday. How many total miles did the track team run on Tuesday and Thursday?

Thought: _____

Information: _____

_____

Number Sentence: _____

Solution Sentence: _____

_____

**9.** Vijay and Melinda made pancakes for breakfast. Vijay put 4 pancakes on the serving plate. Melinda added 4 more pancakes to the plate. How many pancakes were on the serving plate?

Thought: _____

Information: _____

_____

Number Sentence: _____

Solution Sentence: _____

_____

WORK SPACE

**10.** Willy's team hit 3 home runs on Saturday and 7 home runs on Sunday. What was the sum of the home runs hit by Willy's team on Saturday and Sunday?

Thought: _____

Information: _____

_____

Number Sentence: _____

Solution Sentence: _____

_____

WORK SPACE

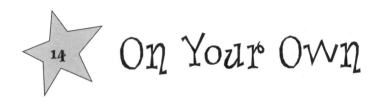

# On Your Own

Use TINS to solve these word problems. Remember to circle key words, draw pictures, and cross out extra information.

---

**1.** Chris collects trading cards and model airplanes. For his birthday his friends gave him 12 trading cards and 7 model airplanes. His sister gave him 5 more trading cards. How many trading cards did Chris receive in all?

┌─── W O R K   S P A C E ───┐
│                           │
│                           │
│                           │
│                           │
│                           │
└───────────────────────────┘

Thought: _____

Information: _____

_____

Number Sentence: _____

Solution Sentence: _____

_____

---

**2.** Jessica agreed to mow Mr. Martinez's lawn for $10. Mr. Martinez was very pleased with Jessica's work, so he added a $2 tip. How much money did Jessica earn?

┌─── W O R K   S P A C E ───┐
│                           │
│                           │
│                           │
│                           │
│                           │
└───────────────────────────┘

T: _____

I: _____

_____

N: _____

S: _____

_____

**3.** The third-graders took a trip to the zoo. They saw 4 grown-up elephants, 3 young monkeys, and 2 baby elephants. How many elephants did the third-graders see in all?

T: _____

I: _____

_____

N: _____

S: _____

_____

WORK SPACE

**4.** Jamal's family went on a vacation. On the first day of their vacation they drove 50 miles. On the second day they drove 130 miles, and on the third day they drove 100 miles. What was the total number of miles Jamal's family drove during the 3 days?

T: _____

I: _____

_____

N: _____

S: _____

_____

WORK SPACE

**5.** Albert is raising money for a school club. During the first week Albert collects $25. The second week he collects $95, and the third week he collects $76. How much money did Albert collect during the first 2 weeks?

T: _____

I: _____

_____

N: _____

S: _____

_____

WORK SPACE

**6.** Cindy is saving money for a new video game. She receives $9 for her allowance, and she earns another $9 for cleaning 7 windows. What is the sum of Cindy's savings now?

T: _____

I: _____

_____

N: _____

S: _____

_____

WORK SPACE

**7.** There are 22 students in Mrs. Owen's class, 17 students in Mrs. Arnold's class, and 25 students in Mr. Lee's class. How many students do these 3 teachers have altogether?

T: _____

I: _____

_____

N: _____

S: _____

_____

WORK SPACE

**8.** Jaime's family went to the school carnival. They spent $19 on lunch, $14 on carnival rides, $6 on souvenirs, and $29 on dinner. What was the sum of money Jaime's family spent on lunch and dinner?

T: _____

I: _____

_____

N: _____

S: _____

_____

WORK SPACE

**9.** There are 17 players on the Shorthorn baseball team, 14 players on the Jays, and 12 players on the Cardinals. What is the total number of players on the 3 teams?

T: _____

I: _____

_____

N: _____

S: _____

_____

WORK SPACE

**10.** The Howard family is traveling to Florida. Mrs. Howard pays $101 for her airline ticket and $101 for Mr. Howard's ticket. Their daughter's ticket costs $88. How much does it cost for all 3 people to fly to Florida?

T: _____

I: _____

_____

N: _____

S: _____

_____

WORK SPACE

# Take the Challenge

Use TINS to solve these word problems.

---

**1.** Liliana played hockey for 3 hours on Monday and 2 hours on Tuesday. How many hours did she play hockey in all?

Thought: _____

Information: _____

_____

Number Sentence: _____

Solution Sentence: _____

_____

> WORK SPACE

---

**2.** When Tyree came home from school, he read a book for two hours. For a snack he ate one taco and drank one glass of juice. For dinner he ate two more tacos. How many tacos did Tyree eat in all?

T: _____

I: _____

_____

N: _____

S: _____

_____

> WORK SPACE

**3.** Coretta bought seven notebooks for the fall semester and eight notebooks for the spring semester. What was the total number of notebooks bought by Coretta?

T: _____

I: _____

_____

N: _____

S: _____

_____

WORK SPACE

---

**4.** Roy weighs 62 pounds. His brother weighs 78 pounds, and his sister weighs 75 pounds. How much do the 2 brothers weigh altogether?

T: _____

I: _____

_____

N: _____

S: _____

_____

WORK SPACE

**5.** It rained for nine days in May, five days in June, and four days in July. What was the sum of the rainy days for the three months?

T: _____

I: _____

_____

N: _____

S: _____

_____

WORK SPACE

**6.** Tasha bought a used computer for $155 and a used printer for $89. How much money did she spend in all?

T: _____

I: _____

_____

N: _____

S: _____

_____

WORK SPACE

**7.** Three girls were saving money. Tammy saved $22, Meredith saved $19, and Ming saved $13. How much money did Meredith and Ming save altogether?

T: _____

I: _____

_____

N: _____

S: _____

_____

WORK SPACE

**8.** In Boston it snowed 4 inches on Monday, 0 inches on Tuesday, 2 inches on Wednesday, and 5 inches on Thursday. What was the total snowfall for Tuesday and Thursday?

T: _____

I: _____

_____

N: _____

S: _____

_____

WORK SPACE

**9.** Mrs. Chen bought twenty-two strawberries and thirty-two cherries. How much fruit did she buy in all?

T: _____

I: _____

_____

N: _____

S: _____

_____

WORK SPACE

**10.** Yolanda's sewing kit contains 6 needles, 13 spools of thread, and 9 buttons. How many needles and buttons does Yolanda have altogether?

T: _____

I: _____

_____

N: _____

S: _____

_____

WORK SPACE

**11.** Ms. Thompson drove 7 miles to school, 2 miles to the grocery store, and 8 miles home. How many total miles did Ms. Thompson drive?

T: _____

I: _____

_____

N: _____

S: _____

_____

WORK SPACE

**12.** During summer vacation James bought 23 ice-cream cones, and Ricardo bought 19 ice-cream cones. How many ice-cream cones did the boys buy in all?

T: _____

I: _____

_____

N: _____

S: _____

_____

WORK SPACE

ADDITION: TAKE THE CHALLENGE

**13.** Jeanette has seven pencils, four pens, a ruler, and some paper clips in her desk. How many pencils and pens does Jeanette have altogether?

T: _____

I: _____

_____

N: _____

S: _____

_____

WORK SPACE

**14.** Fernando jogged 3 miles on Monday, 5 miles on Wednesday, and 4 miles on Friday. How many miles did he jog in all?

T: _____

I: _____

_____

N: _____

S: _____

_____

WORK SPACE

**15.** The Simpsons have 3 dogs, 2 cats, and 4 birds. What is the total number of pets the Simpsons have?

T: _____

I: _____

_____

N: _____

S: _____

_____

WORK SPACE

---

**16.** Quentin usually earns $7 each week for his allowance. This week his dad adds an extra $2 to his allowance. How much money does Quentin earn this week?

T: _____

I: _____

_____

N: _____

S: _____

_____

WORK SPACE

**17.** Ms. Johnson assigned 25 math problems for homework on Wednesday, 50 problems on Thursday, and 35 problems on Friday. What was the total number of math problems she assigned on Thursday and Friday?

T: _____

I: _____

_____

N: _____

S: _____

_____

WORK SPACE

**18.** Keisha practiced in the batting cage for three hours on Saturday and four hours on Sunday. What was the total number of hours Keisha spent in the batting cage?

T: _____

I: _____

_____

N: _____

S: _____

_____

WORK SPACE

**19.** Tara bought a book for $4, a fancy pencil for $1, and a bag of banana chips for $2. How much did Tara spend altogether on the book and the pencil?

T: _____

I: _____

_____

N: _____

S: _____

_____

**20.** The Marcus family skied for 5 hours on Saturday and 6 hours on Sunday. How many total hours did the Marcus family spend skiing?

T: _____

I: _____

_____

N: _____

S: _____

_____

# Write Your Own I

Use the information provided to write your own addition word problems. Then use TINS to solve each problem. Challenge your friends to solve some of the problems you create!

Example: Lindsey had 18 cookies. Susie had 12 cookies. Matt had 2 loaves of bread.

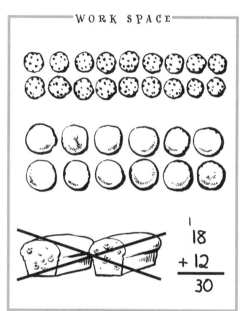

WORK SPACE

Question: _Lindsey made (18 chocolate-chip cookies) for the school bake sale. Susie made (12 oatmeal cookies,) and ~~Matt baked 2 loaves of banana bread~~. How many (cookies) did the girls bake (in all?)_

Thought: ___+___

Information: _Lindsey: 18 cookies, Susie: 12 cookies_

Number Sentence: _18 + 12 =_

Solution Sentence: _The girls baked 30 cookies in all._

In the work space:
```
  1
  18
+ 12
-----
  30
```

**1.** Janey scored 7 points. Tina scored 12 points.

WORK SPACE

Question: _____

_____

_____

_____

Thought: _____

Information: _____

_____

Number Sentence: _____

Solution Sentence: _____

_____

**2.** Flora had three baseball cards. Jamal gave her two baseball cards.

WORK SPACE

Question: _____

_____

_____

_____

T: _____

I: _____

_____

N: _____

S: _____

_____

**3.** Mrs. Willis has 23 students in her class.
Mr. Garza has 18 students in his class. Ms. Wang
has 20 students in her class.

Question: _____

_____

_____

_____

T: _____

I: _____

_____

N: _____

S: _____

_____

# Write Your Own II

Write your own addition word problems. Then use TINS to solve them. Remember to draw a picture, circle key words, and cross out information that isn't important. Happy problem writing!

**1.** Question: _____

_____

_____

_____

Thought: _____

Information: _____

_____

Number Sentence: _____

Solution Sentence: _____

_____

WORK SPACE

**2.** Question: _____

_____

_____

_____

T: _____

I: _____

_____

N: _____

S: _____

_____

WORK SPACE

**3.** Question: _____

_____

_____

_____

T: _____

I: _____

_____

N: _____

S: _____

_____

WORK SPACE

---

**4.** Question: _____

_____

_____

_____

T: _____

I: _____

_____

N: _____

S: _____

_____

WORK SPACE

**5.** Question: _____

_____

_____

_____

T: _____

I: _____

_____

N: _____

S: _____

_____

WORK SPACE

# Explain

Use TINS to solve each word problem. Then write at least 2 sentences explaining how you solved the problem.

Example: Marcella has $18 in her piggy bank. She earns $2 for cleaning the garage. What is the total amount of money Marcella has now?

Thought: _____+_____

Information: ___Marcella has $18,___
_____earns $2 more___

Number Sentence: ___18 + 2 =___

Solution Sentence: ___Marcella has $20.___

Explanation: ___I know that Marcella___
___earned money cleaning. So the___
___amount of money she has will___
___increase. The word "total" also___
___gives me the clue to add.___

WORK SPACE

**1.** Julio is training for a swim meet. He swims eight miles during the first week of training and eleven miles during the second week of training. How many miles does Julio swim in all?

Thought: _____

Information: _____

_____

Number Sentence: _____

Solution Sentence: _____

_____

Explanation: _____

_____

_____

_____

WORK SPACE

**2.** There are 21 students in Ms. Bhutto's class, 23 students in Mr. Cho's class, and 25 students in Mrs. Watson's class. What is the sum of the students in the 3 classes?

T: _____

I: _____

_____

N: _____

S: _____

_____

Explanation: _____

_____

_____

_____

WORK SPACE

# Solving Subtraction Word Problems with TINS

You can use TINS to solve subtraction word problems, too! Keep your eyes open for subtraction key words like these:

- ⚷ left
- ⚷ give (and gave) away
- ⚷ difference
- ⚷ how many more
- ⚷ how much more
- ⚷ subtract

Can you think of any other subtraction key words? If so, add them to the list.

When you see a subtraction key word in a problem, circle it and write – above the key word. Then write – on the THOUGHT line. Next circle and write down the important INFORMATION from the word problem. Sometimes it helps to draw a picture of the important information. It's also a good idea to cross out extra information that doesn't seem important to the problem. Now write your information as a NUMBER SENTENCE. Then plug your answer into your SOLUTION SENTENCE.

Example: Carlos bakes (18 oatmeal cookies.) He (eats 11) of the them. How many (cookies) does Carlos have (left?)

Thought: _____ – _____

Information: __ 18 cookies, _____

___ eats 11 cookies _____

Number Sentence: ___ 18 – 11 = _____

Solution Sentence: ___ Carlos has _____

___ 7 cookies left. _____

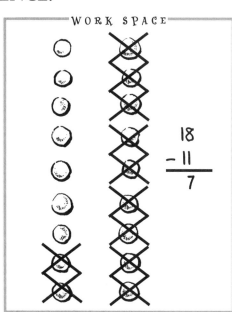

WORK SPACE

$$\begin{array}{r} 18 \\ -11 \\ \hline 7 \end{array}$$

# Try It Out

Use TINS to solve these word problems. Remember to circle key words, draw pictures, and cross out extra information. The first 5 problems have pictures to help you

**1.** Teneisha's cat had 10 kittens. Teneisha gave away 7 of the kittens. How many kittens does Teneisha have now?

WORK SPACE

Thought: _____

Information: _____

_____

Number Sentence: _____

Solution Sentence: _____

_____

**2.** Bianca has $4 in her wallet. Grace has $2 in her pocket. Chad has $11 in his backpack. How much more money does Chad have than Grace?

WORK SPACE

$4    $2    $11

T: _____

I: _____

_____

N: _____

S: _____

_____

**3.** Suzanne brought 24 cupcakes for her class's bake sale. Javier brought 20 cupcakes. What is the difference between the number of cupcakes Suzanne brought and the number of cupcakes Javier brought?

T: _____

I: _____

_____

N: _____

S: _____

_____

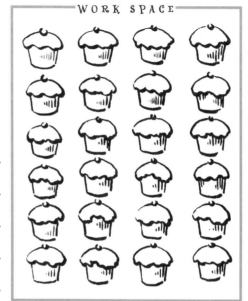

W O R K   S P A C E

**4.** Hannah played 15 softball games in May and 18 games in June. How many more softball games did Hannah play in June than in May?

T: _____

I: _____

_____

N: _____

S: _____

_____

W O R K   S P A C E

**5.** Molly earns $6 each week for her allowance. Her mother subtracted $3 from this week's allowance because Molly forgot to take out the trash. How much money did Molly earn this week?

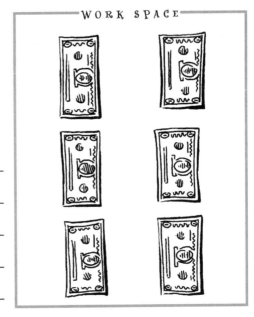

WORK SPACE

T: _____

I: _____

_____

N: _____

S: _____

_____

**6.** Wesley has 11 comic books. A friend borrows 7 of his comic books. How many comic books does Wesley have left?

WORK SPACE

T: _____

I: _____

_____

N: _____

S: _____

_____

**7.** Mrs. Mochal provided 72 prizes for the carnival. Mr. Weinstein provided 19 prizes for the carnival. What is the difference between the number of prizes provided by Mrs. Mochal and the number provided by Mr. Weinstein?

WORK SPACE

T: _____

I: _____

_____

N: _____

S: _____

_____

**8.** Tyrone had 7 pieces of paper and 2 pens. He gave a friend 2 pieces of paper. How many pieces of paper does Tyrone have now?

WORK SPACE

T: _____

I: _____

_____

N: _____

S: _____

_____

**9.** Miriam saved $78. Mark saved $49. How much more money did Miriam save?

T: _____

I: _____

_____

N: _____

S: _____

_____

WORK SPACE

**10.** Audrey did 2 hours of homework on Monday, 1 hour on Tuesday, 3 hours on Wednesday, and 2 hours on Thursday. How many more hours of homework did Audrey do on Wednesday than on Tuesday?

T: _____

I: _____

_____

N: _____

S: _____

_____

WORK SPACE

# On Your Own

Use TINS to solve these word problems. Remember to circle key words, draw pictures, and cross out extra information.

---

**1.** The Shermans drove 188 miles on Monday and 233 miles on Tuesday. How many more miles did the Shermans drive on Tuesday?

Thought: _____

Information: _____

_____

Number Sentence: _____

Solution Sentence: _____

_____

WORK SPACE

---

**2.** Joel has $56. He spends $33 on new school clothes. How much money does Joel have left?

T: _____

I: _____

_____

N: _____

S: _____

_____

WORK SPACE

**3.** Susan B. Anthony Elementary School has
145 students, and 213 students attend Hillcrest
Elementary School. What is the difference in the
number of students who attend the schools?

T: _____

I: _____

_____

N: _____

S: _____

_____

WORK SPACE

**4.** Esperanza has 7 notebooks and 3 colored
pencils. Alexander has 5 pens and 22 colored
pencils. How many more colored pencils does
Alexander have?

T: _____

I: _____

_____

N: _____

S: _____

_____

WORK SPACE

**5.** Marissa's second-grade class went on a field trip to pick apples. Marissa picked 71 apples, and Joanna picked 78 apples. How many more apples did Joanna pick?

T: _____

I: _____

_____

N: _____

S: _____

_____

WORK SPACE

**6.** A bookstore has 129 used paperbacks. The store's owner sells 77 paperbacks at a used-book sale. How many used paperbacks does the owner have left?

T: _____

I: _____

_____

N: _____

S: _____

_____

WORK SPACE

**7.** Sarah and Keenan are playing a board game. Sarah has 79 points, and Keenan has 75 points. Sarah lands on a square that tells her to subtract 9 points from her score. How many points does Sarah have now?

T: _____

I: _____

_____

N: _____

S: _____

_____

WORK SPACE

**8.** The summer months in Pablo's home state of Texas are hot! In June, the temperature soared over 100°F on 22 days. In July, 28 days were hotter than 100°F. How many more days over 100°F were there in July?

T: _____

I: _____

_____

N: _____

S: _____

_____

WORK SPACE

**9.** A flock of 10 blue jays was perched on the branches of an oak tree. A dog scared 6 of the blue jays away. How many blue jays were left on the tree's branches?

T: _____

I: _____

_____

N: _____

S: _____

_____

WORK SPACE

**10.** The cafeteria has 213 chairs. Mrs. Campos moves 88 chairs out of the cafeteria for the science fair. How many chairs are left in the cafeteria?

T: _____

I: _____

_____

N: _____

S: _____

_____

WORK SPACE

# Take the Challenge

Use TINS to solve these word problems.

---

**1.** Matio has 5 yo-yos and 27 hockey trading cards. He trades 14 hockey cards for 5 football cards and a football helmet. How many hockey cards does Matio have now?

WORK SPACE

Thought: _____

Information: _____

_____

Number Sentence: _____

Solution Sentence: _____

_____

---

**2.** Gaylon wrote 29 pages in his writing journal. Cynthia wrote 19 pages in her writing journal. How many more pages did Gaylon write in his journal?

WORK SPACE

T: _____

I: _____

_____

N: _____

S: _____

_____

**3.** Yukiko has thirty-five books and three picture albums on her bookshelf. She loans her friends nineteen books. How many books are left on her bookshelf?

WORK SPACE

T: _____

I: _____

_____

N: _____

S: _____

_____

**4.** During the fall Mr. Park's class read 201 books. Mrs. Nolle's class read 101 books. What is the difference in the number of books each class read?

WORK SPACE

T: _____

I: _____

_____

N: _____

S: _____

_____

**5.** Janice has $121 in her savings account. She withdraws $48 to buy a bicycle helmet. How much money does Janice have now?

T: _____

I: _____

_____

N: _____

S: _____

_____

WORK SPACE

---

**6.** The track team ran eleven miles on Monday, six miles on Tuesday, and seven miles on Wednesday. How many more miles did the track team run on Monday than on Wednesday?

T: _____

I: _____

_____

N: _____

S: _____

_____

WORK SPACE

**7.** Francie has 76 marbles, and Ryan has 56 marbles. How many more marbles does Francie have?

T: _____

I: _____

_____

N: _____

S: _____

_____

WORK SPACE

**8.** Roberto is 48 inches tall, and Richie is 55 inches tall. What is the difference in the boys' heights?

T: _____

I: _____

_____

N: _____

S: _____

_____

WORK SPACE

**9.** Trudy drew 45 pictures. She taped 34 of them to her bedroom walls. She gave the rest of the pictures to her dad. How many pictures did Trudy give to her dad?

T: _____

I: _____

_____

N: _____

S: _____

_____

---

**10.** Yasmine picked 44 daisies and 20 dandelions. She sold 23 of the daisies for one penny each. How many daisies did she have left?

T: _____

I: _____

_____

N: _____

S: _____

_____

**11.** The Nisimblats traveled 233 miles on Saturday and 345 miles on Sunday. How many more miles did they travel on Sunday?

T: _____

I: _____

_____

N: _____

S: _____

_____

WORK SPACE

**12.** Joey owns a juice stand. He has 66 bottles of juice to sell. If he sells 44 bottles by 3 P.M., how many bottles does he have left to sell?

T: _____

I: _____

_____

N: _____

S: _____

_____

WORK SPACE

**13.** Sasha sent 102 e-mails to her friends during the year. Kelly sent 132 e-mails during the same time period. How many more e-mails did Kelly send?

T: _____

I: _____

_____

N: _____

S: _____

_____

WORK SPACE

---

**14.** Will borrowed 22 books and 2 movies from the library. He read 12 of the books during spring break. How many books does he have left to read?

T: _____

I: _____

_____

N: _____

S: _____

_____

WORK SPACE

**15.** Sanjay has $29. He spends $14 on a baseball cap. How much money does he have now?

T: _____

I: _____

_____

N: _____

S: _____

_____

WORK SPACE

**16.** Angie has $44, and Andrew has $32. What is the difference between the amount of money Angie has and the amount Andrew has?

T: _____

I: _____

_____

N: _____

S: _____

_____

WORK SPACE

**17.** Lane spent seven hours fishing with his dad on Saturday and nine hours fishing with his dad on Sunday. How many more hours did he spend fishing on Sunday?

T: _____

I: _____

_____

N: _____

S: _____

_____

**18.** Max has 42 wooden blocks and 63 plastic blocks. He gives his brother 19 wooden blocks and 25 plastic blocks. How many wooden blocks does Max have now?

T: _____

I: _____

_____

N: _____

S: _____

_____

**19.** Montana collects ribbons. She has 18 red ribbons, 33 blue ribbons, and 39 yellow ribbons. How many more yellow ribbons than red ribbons does Montana have?

T: _____

I: _____

_____

N: _____

S: _____

_____

WORK SPACE

**20.** Marjorie buys sixteen jars of jam from the farmers' market. She gives away eleven of the jars. How many jars of jam does Marjorie have now?

T: _____

I: _____

_____

N: _____

S: _____

_____

WORK SPACE

# Write Your Own I

Use the information provided to write your own subtraction word problems. Then use TINS to solve each problem. Challenge your friends to solve some of the problems you create!

Example: Phoebe has $17. She spends $8.

Question: Phoebe has $17 in her wallet. She spends $8 on new shin guards. How much money does Phoebe have left?

Thought: −

Information: $17 in wallet, $8 spent on shin guards

Number Sentence: 17 − 8 =

Solution Sentence: Phoebe has $9 left.

WORK SPACE

**1.** Brad has 9 cookies. Rosa has 10 cookies. Brad eats 4 cookies.

Question: _____

_____

_____

_____

Thought: _____

Information: _____

_____

Number Sentence: _____

Solution Sentence: _____

_____

WORK SPACE

**2.** Anthony has $43. He spends $21.

Question: _____

_____

_____

_____

T: _____

I: _____

_____

N: _____

S: _____

_____

WORK SPACE

**3.** Bettina has 67 baseball cards. She gives away 54 baseball cards.

Question: _____

_____

_____

_____

T: _____

I: _____

_____

N: _____

S: _____

_____

# Write Your Own II

Write your own subtraction word problems. Then use TINS to solve them. Remember to draw a picture, circle key words, and cross out information that isn't important. Happy problem writing!

**1.** Question: _____

_____

_____

_____

Thought: _____

Information: _____

_____

Number Sentence: _____

Solution Sentence: _____

_____

WORK SPACE

**2.** Question: _____

_____

_____

_____

T: _____

I: _____

_____

N: _____

S: _____

_____

WORK SPACE

**3.** Question: _____

_____

_____

_____

T: _____

I: _____

_____

N: _____

S: _____

_____

WORK SPACE

**4.** Question: _____

_____

_____

_____

T: _____

I: _____

_____

N: _____

S: _____

_____

WORK SPACE

**5.** Question: _____

_____

_____

_____

T: _____

I: _____

_____

N: _____

S: _____

_____

WORK SPACE

 # Explain

Use TINS to solve each word problem. Then write at least 2 sentences explaining how you solved the problem.

---

Example: Fredrick read (43 books) during the school year. Henry ~~read 53 books~~, and Vanessa read (56 books) (How many more books) did (Vanessa read than Fredrick?)

Thought: ___ − ___

Information: Vanessa: 56 books, Fredrick: 43 books

Number Sentence: 56 − 43 =

Solution Sentence: Vanessa read 13 more books than Fredrick.

Explanation: I know you are comparing the number of books Vanessa and Fredrick read, so you must subtract. "How many more" are subtraction key words.

WORK SPACE

$$56 - 43 = 13$$

43 books   53 books   56 books

**1.** Anita has saved $76. She spends $49 on holiday gifts. How much money does Anita have left?

WORK SPACE

Thought: _____

Information: _____

_____

Number Sentence: _____

Solution Sentence: _____

_____

Explanation: _____

_____

_____

_____

**2.** There are 303 students at Martin Luther King Jr. Elementary School. In the middle of the year 13 students move away with their families. How many students remain?

WORK SPACE

T: _____

I: _____

_____

N: _____

S: _____

_____

Explanation: _____

_____

_____

_____

# Addition and Subtraction Mixed Practice

Use TINS to solve the following word problems. Remember to draw pictures, circle key words, and cross out extra information.

---

**1.** Savannah has 19 different-colored barrettes. She loans her younger sister 3 barrettes. How many barrettes does Savannah have left?

WORK SPACE

Thought: _____

Information: _____

_____

Number Sentence: _____

Solution Sentence: _____

_____

---

**2.** Jeffrey invited three friends to a slumber party. His brother invited two more friends to the party. How many friends received invitations in all?

WORK SPACE

T: _____

I: _____

_____

N: _____

S: _____

_____

**3.** Tatiana has 16 goldfish, 3 cats, and 2 dogs. She gives 9 goldfish to her cousin. How many goldfish does Tatiana have left?

T: _____

I: _____

_____

N: _____

S: _____

_____

WORK SPACE

**4.** Desiree has $44 in her savings account. She earns $13 baby-sitting and deposits this money in her account. What is the sum of Desiree's savings now?

T: _____

I: _____

_____

N: _____

S: _____

_____

WORK SPACE

**5.** Jason took fifteen white shirts, twelve blue shirts, and three yellow shirts to the cleaners. How many more blue shirts than yellow shirts did Jason take to the cleaners?

T: _____

I: _____

_____

N: _____

S: _____

_____

WORK SPACE

**6.** Ms. Cornwell has 23 students in her class, Mr. Baumann has 25 students in his class, and Ms. Kim has 19 students in her class. How many students do the three teachers have altogether?

T: _____

I: _____

_____

N: _____

S: _____

_____

WORK SPACE

**7.** Rachel walked seventeen blocks on Monday, twelve blocks on Tuesday, and thirteen blocks on Wednesday. What was the total number of blocks Rachel walked?

T: _____

I: _____

_____

N: _____

S: _____

_____

WORK SPACE

**8.** Sandra has 29 bonus points. Her teacher subtracts 3 points when Sandra forgets her homework. How many points does Sandra have now?

T: _____

I: _____

_____

N: _____

S: _____

_____

WORK SPACE

**9.** Terrance ran for 56 minutes on Saturday and 43 minutes on Sunday. Each day he ate 2 bananas before he went running. How many more minutes did Terrance run on Saturday than on Sunday?

T: _____

I: _____

_____

N: _____

S: _____

_____

WORK SPACE

---

**10.** Margaret saved $133 over the summer, and Sam saved $254 over the summer. How much more money did Sam save?

T: _____

I: _____

_____

N: _____

S: _____

_____

WORK SPACE

**11.** Marissa read for one hour on Monday, two hours on Tuesday, and four hours on Thursday. How many hours did Marissa read in all?

T: _____

I: _____

_____

N: _____

S: _____

_____

WORK SPACE

**12.** Zachary bought 22 red marbles, 72 green marbles, and 91 beige marbles at the store. What was the total number of beige and red marbles Zachary bought?

T: _____

I: _____

_____

N: _____

S: _____

_____

WORK SPACE

**13.** Wazir scored 12 points during the basketball game. Mariah scored 28 points during the same game. What is the difference between the number of points Wazir scored and the number of points Mariah scored?

T: _____

I: _____

_____

N: _____

S: _____

_____

WORK SPACE

---

**14.** Last month Jacinda's dog buried 17 bones. This month her dog buried 23 bones. How many bones did Jacinda's dog bury altogether?

T: _____

I: _____

_____

N: _____

S: _____

_____

WORK SPACE

**15.** Franny the frog ate 17 bugs, and Fred the frog ate 37 bugs. How many more bugs did Fred eat?

T: _____

I: _____

_____

N: _____

S: _____

_____

WORK SPACE

---

**16.** A pine tree grew five inches in April and three inches in May. How many more inches did the tree grow in April?

T: _____

I: _____

_____

N: _____

S: _____

_____

WORK SPACE

**17.** Solomon telephoned 7 friends on Friday, 3 friends on Saturday, and 8 friends on Sunday. How many friends did he call in all?

T: _____

I: _____

_____

N: _____

S: _____

_____

WORK SPACE

**18.** Janna has $76, Marla has $32, and Isaac has $89. How much more money does Isaac have than Janna?

T: _____

I: _____

_____

N: _____

S: _____

_____

WORK SPACE

**19.** Chrissy the cat chased 7 mice in the morning and 9 mice in the evening. How many mice did Chrissy chase altogether?

T: _____

I: _____

_____

N: _____

S: _____

_____

WORK SPACE

---

**20.** During the summer months there were forty-nine sunny days, thirty-two rainy days, and eleven partly cloudy days. What was the total number of days during which it did not rain?

T: _____

I: _____

_____

N: _____

S: _____

_____

WORK SPACE

# Solving Multiplication Word Problems with TINS

Are multiplication word problems getting you down? Have no fear: TINS is here! Below are some key words that appear in multiplication word problems:

- ⚷ **groups** (and other words that are kinds of groups)
  Examples: *groups* of campers, *batches* of cookies, *bunches* of grapes, *bags* of groceries, *litters* of kittens

- ⚷ **each** *Each* is a tricky key word because it shows up in division problems, too. You'll know you are most likely reading a multiplication problem if *each* shows up with one of its buddies: *altogether, in all,* or *total.*

Do you know any other multiplication key words? If you do, you can add them to the list.

When you see a multiplication key word in a problem, circle it and write × above the key word. Then write × on the THOUGHT line. Next circle and write down the important INFORMATION from the word problem. Sometimes it helps to draw a picture of the important information. Now write your information as a NUMBER SENTENCE. Then plug your answer into your SOLUTION SENTENCE.

Example: Martina baked (4 batches of cookies) for a party. There were (8 cookies in each batch.) How many cookies did Martina bake (in all?)

Thought: ___×_____

Information: _4 batches, 8 cookies in_
_____ each batch _____

Number Sentence: _4 × 8 = _____

Solution Sentence: _Martina baked_
_____ 32 cookies in all. _____

WORK SPACE

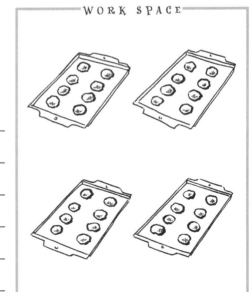

# Try It Out

Use TINS to solve these word problems. Remember to circle key words and draw pictures. The first 5 problems have pictures to help you.

---

**1.** Samantha has 2 green shirts. Each shirt has 6 buttons. What is the total number of buttons on her green shirts?

Thought: _____

Information: _____

_____

Number Sentence: _____

Solution Sentence: _____

_____

WORK SPACE

---

**2.** Jerry picked 3 bunches of daisies. Each bunch had 4 daisies in it. How many daisies did he pick altogether?

T: _____

I: _____

_____

N: _____

S: _____

_____

WORK SPACE

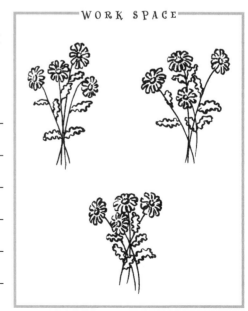

**3.** Mr. Flaherty has 5 jars of jellybeans. Each jar has 9 jellybeans in it. How many jellybeans does Mr. Flaherty have in all?

T: _____

I: _____

_____

N: _____

S: _____

_____

WORK SPACE

**4.** Marcus, Pedro, and Rosanna each save $2. What is the total amount of money the 3 children save?

T: _____

I: _____

_____

N: _____

S: _____

_____

WORK SPACE

**5.** Quatina buys 2 bags of oranges. Each bag has 7 oranges in it. How many oranges does Quatina buy in all?

T: _____

I: _____

_____

N: _____

S: _____

_____

WORK SPACE

**6.** Ebony walked her 2 dogs to the pet store. She bought 2 bones for each dog. How many bones did she buy altogether?

T: _____

I: _____

_____

N: _____

S: _____

_____

WORK SPACE

**7.** Ms. Reed takes her 4 children to the zoo. She buys each child 2 cartons of juice. How many cartons of juice does Ms. Reed buy in all?

T: _____

I: _____

_____

N: _____

S: _____

_____

WORK SPACE

---

**8.** Walter's 3 dogs all have litters of puppies. There are 5 puppies in each litter. How many puppies are there in all?

T: _____

I: _____

_____

N: _____

S: _____

_____

WORK SPACE

**9.** Anthony played in 6 baseball games. He hit 3 home runs in each game. What is the total number of home runs he hit?

T: _____

I: _____

_____

N: _____

S: _____

_____

WORK SPACE

**10.** Sierra has a sticker collection. She puts 10 stickers on each page of her sticker book. What is the total number of stickers on 5 pages of Sierra's book?

T: _____

I: _____

_____

N: _____

S: _____

_____

WORK SPACE

# On Your Own

Use TINS to solve these word problems. Remember to circle key words and draw pictures.

---

**1.** Mr. Bennett has 5 tables in his classroom. Each table is surrounded by 5 chairs. What is the total number of chairs around the tables?

Thought: _____

Information: _____

_____

Number Sentence: _____

Solution Sentence: _____

_____

WORK SPACE

---

**2.** Cynthia buys 6 tickets at the carnival. She can use each ticket for 2 carnival rides. How many rides can Cynthia go on in all?

T: _____

I: _____

_____

N: _____

S: _____

_____

WORK SPACE

**3.** Eduardo has 2 coats. Each coat has 7 brown buttons. What is the total number of buttons on his coats?

T: _____

I: _____

_____

N: _____

S: _____

_____

WORK SPACE

**4.** Four frogs sat on some lily pads in Morse Pond. Each frog hopped 5 times to the center of the pond. How many times did the frogs hop altogether?

T: _____

I: _____

_____

N: _____

S: _____

_____

WORK SPACE

**5.** Lavosha works on her needlepoint 10 minutes for 6 nights in a row. How many minutes does Lavosha spend on her needlepoint in all?

T: _____

I: _____

_____

N: _____

S: _____

_____

**6.** Mrs. Gonzales bought 9 small bags of peanuts. Each bag had 10 peanuts in it. How many peanuts were there in all?

T: _____

I: _____

_____

N: _____

S: _____

_____

**7.** Carla jogs 3 miles each day of the week. What is the total number of miles she jogs in 7 days?

T: _____

I: _____

_____

N: _____

S: _____

_____

WORK SPACE

**8.** Gwen earns 5 cents each time she takes out the trash. Last month she took out the trash 9 times. How much money did she earn in all?

T: _____

I: _____

_____

N: _____

S: _____

_____

WORK SPACE

**9.** Mr. Latour gives music lessons to 3 groups of students. Each group has 4 students in it. How many music students does Mr. Latour have altogether?

T: _____

I: _____

_____

N: _____

S: _____

_____

WORK SPACE

**10.** Elton has 4 toy cars. Each car has 4 wheels. How many wheels are there in all?

T: _____

I: _____

_____

N: _____

S: _____

_____

WORK SPACE

# Take the Challenge

Make a list of the multiplication key words you know.

_____     _____

_____     _____

Remember to look for these words as you use TINS to solve the problems below. Re-check each solution sentence to make sure it makes sense!

**1.** Maria walks 2 miles each day. What is the total number of miles she walks in 5 days?

Thought: _____

Information: _____

_____

Number Sentence: _____

Solution Sentence: _____

_____

WORK SPACE

**2.** Joel invites three friends to his house. They plan to play a game with tennis balls. Each friend brings five tennis balls. How many tennis balls do Joel's friends bring in all?

T: _____

I: _____

_____

N: _____

S: _____

_____

WORK SPACE

**3.** Timothy likes ice cream. He buys 2 cartons of each of his 4 favorite flavors for a party. How many cartons of ice cream does Timothy buy in all?

T: _____

I: _____

_____

N: _____

S: _____

_____

WORK SPACE

---

**4.** Annabelle plays basketball for 3 hours each afternoon for 7 days. What is the total number of hours that she plays basketball?

T: _____

I: _____

_____

N: _____

S: _____

_____

WORK SPACE

**5.** Santiago has 7 autographed baseballs. There are 5 names on each baseball. How many autographs does he have in all?

T: _____

I: _____

_____

N: _____

S: _____

_____

WORK SPACE

**6.** Mr. Ortez makes two trips in his airplane each day for six days. How many trips does Mr. Ortez make in all?

T: _____

I: _____

_____

N: _____

S: _____

_____

WORK SPACE

**7.** Larissa works on her model rocket for 2 hours each day. If she works on her model for 9 days, how many hours does she spend altogether?

T: _____

I: _____

_____

N: _____

S: _____

_____

WORK SPACE

**8.** Francisco helped to load his mom's truck with sacks of grain. He carried a total of seven sacks, and each sack weighed twelve pounds. How many pounds of grain did Francisco carry in all?

T: _____

I: _____

_____

N: _____

S: _____

_____

WORK SPACE

**9.** Jay spends 3 hours per day at the livestock show on Thursday, Friday, Saturday, and Sunday. What is the total number of hours Jay spends at the show during the 4 days?

T: _____

I: _____

_____

N: _____

S: _____

_____

WORK SPACE

---

**10.** During the school year Christopher writes three letters to nine of his closest friends. How many letters does he write in all?

T: _____

I: _____

_____

N: _____

S: _____

_____

WORK SPACE

**11.** Dominique listens to the radio for 2 hours each day. What is the total number of hours she listens to the radio over 5 days?

T: _____

I: _____

_____

N: _____

S: _____

_____

WORK SPACE

---

**12.** Blackshear Elementary School has 3 smoke detectors in every hallway. There are 11 hallways in the school. How many smoke detectors does Blackshear Elementary have in all?

T: _____

I: _____

_____

N: _____

S: _____

_____

WORK SPACE

**13.** Tito's teacher gives lots of homework! Tito has four hours of homework for five nights in a row. How many total hours does he spend on his homework?

T: _____

I: _____

_____

N: _____

S: _____

_____

WORK SPACE

**14.** Mr. Maloney picks 7 bunches of wildflowers. Each bunch has 8 flowers in it. How many flowers does Mr. Maloney pick altogether?

T: _____

I: _____

_____

N: _____

S: _____

_____

WORK SPACE

**15.** Eight easels are in the art room.
Six paintbrushes rest on each easel.
What is the total number of paintbrushes
on the easels?

T: _____

I: _____

_____

N: _____

S: _____

_____

WORK SPACE

**16.** Ortella and Susanna love to watch cartoons.
They watch 2 cartoons each day on Friday,
Saturday, and Sunday. How many cartoons
do the girls watch altogether?

T: _____

I: _____

_____

N: _____

S: _____

_____

WORK SPACE

**17.** J.J. reads three books every week. How many books does he read in five weeks?

WORK SPACE

T: _____

I: _____

_____

N: _____

S: _____

_____

**18.** Keiko collects seashells. She has 4 shoeboxes filled with her shells. Each shoebox has 11 shells in it. What is the total number of seashells in the boxes?

WORK SPACE

T: _____

I: _____

_____

N: _____

S: _____

_____

**19.** Lindsey loves orange juice. She drinks two glasses for breakfast and two glasses for lunch. How many glasses of orange juice does she drink over three days?

T: _____

I: _____

_____

N: _____

S: _____

_____

WORK SPACE

**20.** Roberto has 6 friends. Each friend has 2 sisters and 1 brother. How many sisters do Roberto's friends have altogether?

T: _____

I: _____

_____

N: _____

S: _____

_____

WORK SPACE

# Write Your Own I

Use the information provided to write your own multiplication word problems. Then use TINS to solve each problem. Challenge your friends to solve some of the problems you create!

Example: Leo has 4 bags of groceries. There are 9 items in each bag.

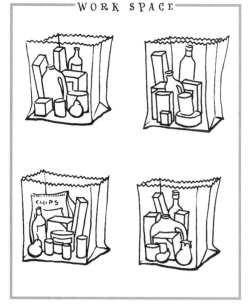

WORK SPACE

Question: Leo unloads (4 bags) of groceries from his mom's car. (Each bag has 9 items in it.) How many grocery items does Leo carry (in all?)

Thought: ×

Information: 4 bags of groceries, 9 items per bag

Number Sentence: 4 × 9 =

Solution Sentence: Leo carries 36 grocery items in all.

**1.** Allison has four cats. Each cat has two bells on its collar.

Question: _____

_____

_____

_____

Thought: _____

Information: _____

_____

Number Sentence: _____

Solution Sentence: _____

_____

WORK SPACE

**2.** Oscar has 6 folders. Each folder has 9 sheets of paper in it.

Question: _____

_____

_____

_____

T: _____

I: _____

_____

N: _____

S: _____

_____

WORK SPACE

**3.** Milagro has choir practice five days each week. Practice lasts two hours.

Question: _____

_____

_____

_____

T: _____

I: _____

_____

N: _____

S: _____

_____

┌─── WORK SPACE ───┐
│                  │
│                  │
│                  │
│                  │
│                  │
│                  │
│                  │
│                  │
│                  │
└──────────────────┘

# Write Your Own II

Write your own multiplication word problems. Then use TINS to solve them. Remember to draw pictures and circle key words. Happy problem writing!

**1.** Question: _____

_____

_____

_____

Thought: _____

Information: _____

_____

Number Sentence: _____

Solution Sentence: _____

_____

WORK SPACE

**2.** Question: _____

_____

_____

_____

T: _____

I: _____

_____

N: _____

S: _____

_____

WORK SPACE

**3.** Question: _____

_____

_____

_____

T: _____

I: _____

_____

N: _____

S: _____

_____

WORK SPACE

**4.** Question: _____

_____

_____

_____

T: _____

I: _____

_____

N: _____

S: _____

_____

WORK SPACE

**5.** Question: _____

_____

_____

_____

T: _____

I: _____

_____

N: _____

S: _____

_____

WORK SPACE

# Explain

Use TINS to solve each word problem. Then write at least 2 sentences explaining how you solved the problem.

Example: Tara plants (4 rows of sunflowers.) She places (7 sunflower seeds in each row.) How many sunflowers does Tara plant (in all?)

Thought:  ✕ _____

Information:  4 rows, 7 sunflowers
in each row

Number Sentence:  4 × 7 =

Solution Sentence:  Tara plants
28 sunflowers in all.

Explanation:  I know Tara planted
4 groups of 7, so I need to multiply.
When I drew a picture, I saw that
Tara planted 28 sunflowers.

WORK SPACE

**1.** Ms. Desjardins buys seven books of stamps. Each book has ten stamps in it. How many stamps does Ms. Desjardins buy in all?

Thought : _____

Information: _____

_____

Number Sentence: _____

Solution Sentence: _____

_____

Explanation: _____

_____

_____

_____

WORK SPACE

**2.** Willis has 6 shelves in his room. Each shelf holds 12 books. How many books does Willis have altogether?

T: _____

I: _____

_____

N: _____

S: _____

_____

Explanation: _____

_____

_____

_____

WORK SPACE

# Solving Division Word Problems with TINS

If TINS can help you with addition, subtraction, and multiplication word problems, then....You guessed it! TINS can help you conquer division word problems, too. Check out these division key words:

- 🔑 divide
- 🔑 equal
- 🔑 equally
- 🔑 separate
- 🔑 each
- 🔑 evenly

*Each* is that pesky key word that also appears in multiplication word problems. If *each* appears with another division key word, such as *divide* or *equally,* then you're probably dealing with a division problem.

Can you think of any other division key words? If so, add them to the list.

When you see a division key word in a problem, circle it and write ÷ above the key word. Then write ÷ on the THOUGHT line. Next circle and write down the important INFORMATION from the word problem. Sometimes it helps to draw a picture of the important information. Now write your information as a NUMBER SENTENCE. Then plug your answer into your SOLUTION SENTENCE.

Example: Molly has (15 crayons.) She wants to share the crayons (equally) with Petra and Luis. How many crayons will each of the (3 children) get?

WORK SPACE

Thought: ÷ _____

Information: 15 crayons,

_____ 3 children

Number Sentence: 15 ÷ 3 =

Solution Sentence: Each child will get

5 crayons.

Use TINS to solve these word problems. Remember to circle key words and draw pictures. The first 5 problems have pictures to help you.

---

**1.** Mr. Luthke bought 6 peanut-butter cookies for his 2 children. He wants to give an equal number of cookies to them. How many peanut-butter cookies will each child receive?

WORK SPACE

Thought: _____

Information: _____

_____

Number Sentence: _____

Solution Sentence: _____

_____

---

**2.** Aisha walks her 3 dogs to the pet store. She buys 9 bones and wants to divide them evenly among her dogs. How many bones will each dog get?

WORK SPACE

T: _____

I: _____

_____

N: _____

S: _____

_____

**3.** Barbara orders a large pizza. The pizza is cut into 8 slices. Barbara and her brother eat equal shares of the pizza, and there are no leftovers. How many slices of pizza does each of them eat?

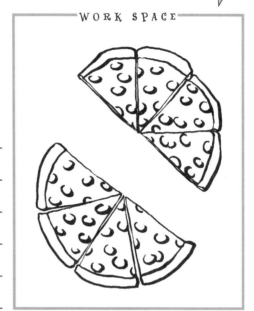

WORK SPACE

T: _____

I: _____

_____

N: _____

S: _____

_____

**4.** Ted collects 30 leaves for his science project. He wants to separate them and glue 5 leaves onto each sheet of paper. How many sheets of paper will he need?

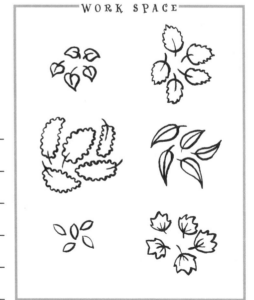

WORK SPACE

T: _____

I: _____

_____

N: _____

S: _____

_____

**5.** Ms. Washington buys 12 balloons for a birthday party. She gives an equal number to each of the 4 children at the party, and she doesn't keep any of the balloons for herself. How many balloons does each child receive?

WORK SPACE

T: _____

I: _____

_____

N: _____

S: _____

_____

**6.** Melanie has $18 to spend during vacation. She wants to divide her money, so that she has an equal amount to spend on her 3 vacation days. How much money should Melanie spend each day?

WORK SPACE

T: _____

I: _____

_____

N: _____

S: _____

_____

**7.** Toby checks out 12 books from the library. He divides them equally between his twin sister and himself. How many books does each child have?

T: _____

I: _____

_____

N: _____

S: _____

_____

WORK SPACE

**8.** On a hot summer day Cynthia makes 60 ounces of lemonade. She pours equal amounts of the lemonade into 6 glasses, and there is no lemonade leftover. How much lemonade is in each glass?

T: _____

I: _____

_____

N: _____

S: _____

_____

WORK SPACE

**9.** Tiana mails 3 postcards. If she mails an equal number of postcards to Carmelita, Karen, and Robert, how many postcards does each of her friends receive?

T: _____

I: _____

_____

N: _____

S: _____

_____

WORK SPACE

**10.** Steven has 8 cups of flour. He divides the flour evenly to use in 4 different recipes. How many cups of flour does he use for each recipe?

T: _____

I: _____

_____

N: _____

S: _____

_____

WORK SPACE

# On Your Own

Use TINS to solve these word problems. Remember to circle key words and draw pictures.

**1.** Tamara and her 3 friends decide to work on a jigsaw puzzle. The puzzle has 36 pieces. The children want to divide the pieces equally. How many puzzle pieces will each of the 4 friends get?

Thought: _____

Information: _____

_____

Number Sentence: _____

Solution Sentence: _____

_____

WORK SPACE

**2.** Mrs. Castro sets aside $12 a week for her 3 children's allowances. She gives each child the same amount of money. How much money does each child receive for an allowance?

T: _____

I: _____

_____

N: _____

S: _____

_____

WORK SPACE

**3.** Delicia has 6 hours to spend with her 3 best friends. She wants to spend an equal amount of time alone with each friend. How many hours should she spend with each friend?

WORK SPACE

T: _____

I: _____

_____

N: _____

S: _____

_____

**4.** Saul separates his 10 action figures into 2 equal piles. How many action figures are in each pile?

WORK SPACE

T: _____

I: _____

_____

N: _____

S: _____

_____

**5.** The librarian buys 50 new books for the library. She puts 10 books on each bookshelf. How many bookshelves will the librarian use?

T: _____

I: _____

_____

N: _____

S: _____

_____

WORK SPACE

---

**6.** Ms. Stevens prepares 45 orange slices for soccer practice. If 9 team members show up for practice and share the oranges evenly, how many slices does each player get?

T: _____

I: _____

_____

N: _____

S: _____

_____

WORK SPACE

**7.** Joanne picks 27 flowers. She wants to divide them into 3 equal bunches. How many flowers does she put in each bunch?

T: _____

I: _____

_____

N: _____

S: _____

_____

WORK SPACE

**8.** Two shuttle buses arrive to take 50 students home. The bus drivers want to divide the students equally between the 2 buses. How many students will ride on each bus?

T: _____

I: _____

_____

N: _____

S: _____

_____

WORK SPACE

**9.** Pete counted 40 parked cars as he walked 4 blocks to his apartment building. An equal number of cars were parked on each block. How many cars were on each block?

T: _____

I: _____

_____

N: _____

S: _____

_____

WORK SPACE

**10.** Shirley bought 25 notebooks for her 5 sons. How many notebooks will each son get if the notebooks are divided evenly?

T: _____

I: _____

_____

N: _____

S: _____

_____

WORK SPACE

# Take the Challenge

Make a list of the division key words you know.

| | |
|---|---|
| _____ | _____ |
| _____ | _____ |
| _____ | _____ |

Remember to look for these words as you use TINS to solve the problems below. Re-check each solution sentence to make sure it makes sense!

**1.** Sheila plans to spend $24 on gifts for her 3 sisters. She wants to spend an equal sum of money on each of them. How much should she spend on each gift?

Thought: _____

Information: _____

_____

Number Sentence: _____

Solution Sentence: _____

_____

WORK SPACE

**2.** Forty-nine newspapers are delivered to seven houses during the week. If an equal number of newspapers are delivered to each house, how many newspapers does each house receive?

T: _____

I: _____

_____

N: _____

S: _____

_____

WORK SPACE

**3.** Mr. Thomas grilled 8 hamburgers for dinner. The 4 members of the Thomas family polished off all the hamburgers, and each person ate the same number of burgers. How many burgers did each family member eat?

T: _____

I: _____

_____

N: _____

S: _____

_____

WORK SPACE

**4.** Thirty students sign up for gymnastics class. The students are divided into two equal groups. How many students are in each group?

WORK SPACE

T: _____

I: _____

_____

N: _____

S: _____

_____

**5.** Nia's grandpa spent 10 hours on the telephone over the course of 5 days. If he spent an equal amount of time on the telephone each day, how many hours did he talk per day?

WORK SPACE

T: _____

I: _____

_____

N: _____

S: _____

_____

**6.** William has forty-two noisemakers. He separates them into seven equal stacks and puts each stack into a party favor bag. How many noisemakers are in each bag?

T: _____

I: _____

_____

N: _____

S: _____

_____

WORK SPACE

**7.** Geraldine wins six prizes at the state fair. She wants to give the same number of prizes to each of her six brothers. How many prizes should she give to each of them?

T: _____

I: _____

_____

N: _____

S: _____

_____

WORK SPACE

**8.** Randall had twenty-two basketball cards. He shared them equally with Philip. How many basketball cards did each boy have?

WORK SPACE

T: _____

I: _____

_____

N: _____

S: _____

_____

**9.** A doctor has 56 boxes of bandages. She separates the boxes into equal piles and puts them into 8 different cabinets. How many boxes of bandages did she place in each cabinet?

WORK SPACE

T: _____

I: _____

_____

N: _____

S: _____

_____

**10.** The ten contestants in a pie-eating contest gobbled up thirty apple pies. If each contestant ate an equal number of pies, how many pies did each person eat?

T: _____

I: _____

_____

N: _____

S: _____

_____

WORK SPACE

**11.** The homework center has 6 tutors. Each tutor works with the same number of students. If 12 students go to the homework center, how many students will each tutor have?

T: _____

I: _____

_____

N: _____

S: _____

_____

WORK SPACE

**12.** A baker bakes 16 birthday cakes. He plans to let the cakes cool on platters. If 4 cakes fit on each platter, how many platters will he need?

T: _____

I: _____

_____

N: _____

S: _____

_____

WORK SPACE

---

**13.** The hockey team scored 2 goals in the final game. If Evan and Amy scored the same number of goals in the game, how many goals did each player score?

T: _____

I: _____

_____

N: _____

S: _____

_____

WORK SPACE

**14.** Last weekend Ernie rode his bicycle for 8 hours. If he bicycled for an equal amount of time on Saturday and Sunday, how many hours did he bike per day?

WORK SPACE

T: _____

I: _____

_____

N: _____

S: _____

_____

**15.** Adam separates his dirty laundry into three equal piles. If he has eighteen dirty items, how many are in each pile?

WORK SPACE

T: _____

I: _____

_____

N: _____

S: _____

_____

**16.** Leah and her dad are going on vacation. They drive thirty-six hours over a four-day period. Leah's dad drives the same number of hours each day. How many hours does he drive per day?

T: _____

I: _____

_____

N: _____

S: _____

_____

WORK SPACE

**17.** Mr. Seymour has 12 children in his class. He orders 48 frog stickers for homework awards. He wants to divide the stickers evenly among his students. How many frog stickers will each child get?

T: _____

I: _____

_____

N: _____

S: _____

_____-

_____

WORK SPACE

**18.** Ruth, David, and Antonio caught 24 fish. If each child caught an equal number of fish, how many fish did each child catch?

WORK SPACE

T: _____

I: _____

_____

N: _____

S: _____

_____

**19.** Eighty students are enrolled in the third grade at Lanier Elementary School. If the students are divided equally into four classes, how many students are in each class?

WORK SPACE

T: _____

I: _____

_____

N: _____

S: _____

_____

**20.** Ms. Honan has three sons and one daughter. She purchases twelve new T-shirts for her children. If the children divide the shirts evenly, how many new shirts will each child receive?

T: _____

I: _____

_____

N: _____

S: _____

_____

# Write Your Own I

Use the information provided to write your own division word problems. Then use TINS to solve each problem. Challenge your friends to solve some of the problems you create!

Example: Maya hit 12 home runs. She played in 6 games.

Question: __Maya's team played__ __6 softball games. She hit 12 home runs__ __in the games. If she hit an equal__ __number of home runs in each game,__ __how many home runs did Maya hit__ __per game?__

Thought: __÷__

Information: __12 home runs,__ __6 games__

Number Sentence: __12 ÷ 6 =__

Solution Sentence: __Maya hit 2 home__ __runs in each game.__

WORK SPACE

**1.** Nicholas has ten apples. He eats them in five days.

WORK SPACE

Question: _____

_____

_____

_____

Thought: _____

Information: _____

_____

Number Sentence: _____

Solution Sentence: _____

_____

**2.** A classroom has 24 chairs. There are 2 chairs at each desk.

WORK SPACE

Question: _____

_____

_____

_____

T: _____

I: _____

_____

N: _____

S: _____

_____

**3.** The gym teacher has 9 balls. The class has 27 students.

Question: _____

_____

_____

_____

T: _____

I: _____

_____

N: _____

S: _____

_____

WORK SPACE

# Write Your Own II

Write your own division word problems. Then use TINS to solve them. Remember to draw pictures and circle key words. Happy problem writing!

**1.** Question: _____

_____

_____

_____

Thought: _____

Information: _____

_____

Number Sentence: _____

Solution Sentence: _____

_____

WORK SPACE

**2.** Question: _____

_____

_____

_____

T: _____

I: _____

_____

N: _____

S: _____

_____

WORK SPACE

**3.** Question: _____

_____

_____

_____

T: _____

I: _____

_____

N: _____

S: _____

_____

WORK SPACE

**4.** Question: _____

_____

_____

_____

T: _____

I: _____

_____

N: _____

S: _____

_____

WORK SPACE

**5.** Question: _____

_____

_____

_____

T: _____

I: _____

_____

N: _____

S: _____

_____

WORK SPACE

# Explain

Use TINS to solve each word problem. Then write at least 2 sentences explaining how you solved the problem.

Example: Daniel buys (eighteen bones.) He plans to (divide) the bones (equally) among his (three) (dogs.) How many bones will each dog get?

Thought: ___÷_____

Information: __18 bones, 3 dogs_____

_____

Number Sentence: __18 ÷ 3 =_____

Solution Sentence: __Each dog will get__

___6 bones._____

Explanation: __I know that Daniel is__

__dividing the bones into 3 equal__

__groups. When I divide the 18 bones__

__into 3 equal groups, I see that each__

__dog gets 6 bones._____

WORK SPACE

**1.** Mr. Santos wins four stuffed animals at the street carnival. He divides the stuffed animals evenly between his two children. How many stuffed animals does each child receive?

Thought: _____

Information: _____

_____

Number Sentence: _____

Solution Sentence: _____

_____

Explanation: _____

_____

_____

_____

WORK SPACE

**2.** Audrey has 24 pictures left on her roll of film. She plans to use the rest of the film to take pictures at a birthday party and a wedding ceremony. If she wants to take an equal number of pictures at the party and the wedding, how many pictures should she take at each event?

T: _____

I: _____

_____

N: _____

S: _____

_____

Explanation: _____

_____

_____

_____

WORK SPACE

# Multiplication and Division Mixed Practice

Use TINS to solve these problems. Remember to circle key words and draw pictures.

**1.** Lynn has four letters to mail. She places each letter in its own envelope. Then she puts two stamps on each envelope. How many stamps does Lynn use in all?

Thought: _____

Information: _____

_____

Number Sentence: _____

Solution Sentence: _____

_____

WORK SPACE

**2.** Doug purchases 24 pens. He divides his pens into 3 equal groups and stores them in 3 supply boxes. How many pens does he store in each box?

T: _____

I: _____

_____

N: _____

S: _____

_____

WORK SPACE

**3.** Virginia wants to decorate six walls in her apartment. She hangs three pictures on each of the six walls. How many pictures does she hang in all?

T: _____

I: _____

_____

N: _____

S: _____

_____

WORK SPACE

**4.** There are 8 schools in the city. Each school has 2 parking lots. How many parking lots do the schools have altogether?

WORK SPACE

T: _____

I: _____

_____

N: _____

S: _____

_____

**5.** Six robins lay five eggs each. How many eggs are there in all?

WORK SPACE

T: _____

I: _____

_____

N: _____

S: _____

_____

**6.** Ms. Peron baked a cherry pie and divided it into 10 slices. The 5 members of the Peron family ate the pie for dessert. Each person ate an equal number of slices, and there were no leftovers. How many slices of pie did each person eat?

WORK SPACE

T: _____

I: _____

_____

N: _____

S: _____

_____

**7.** A baby-sitter club is hired to baby-sit for fifty-six hours during the month of March. The eight members of the club decide to divide the work evenly. How many hours will each member baby-sit?

WORK SPACE

T: _____

I: _____

_____

N: _____

S: _____

_____

**8.** Vanessa draws fifteen happy faces. Each happy face has two eyes. How many eyes does Vanessa draw in all?

T: _____

I: _____

_____

N: _____

S: _____

_____

WORK SPACE

**9.** A small tree in Pamela's yard has 9 branches. If there are 11 blossoms on each branch, how many blossoms does the tree have altogether?

T: _____

I: _____

_____

N: _____

S: _____

_____

WORK SPACE

**10.** Carl makes 12 sandwiches for a picnic. If he and his 3 friends share the sandwiches equally, how many sandwiches will each of the 4 children eat?

WORK SPACE

T: _____

I: _____

_____

N: _____

S: _____

_____

**11.** George gave eighty-one grapes to his nine friends. If he gave each friend an equal number of grapes, how many grapes did each friend get?

WORK SPACE

T: _____

I: _____

_____

N: _____

S: _____

_____

**12.** Rhonda's shirt is decorated with 72 stars. There are 8 rows of stars, and each row has the same number of stars in it. How many stars are in each row?

T: _____

I: _____

_____

N: _____

S: _____

_____

WORK SPACE

**13.** Seven children go to a party. Each child receives a goody bag with three wind-up toys in it. What is the total number of wind-up toys that the children receive?

T: _____

I: _____

_____

N: _____

S: _____

_____

WORK SPACE

**14.** Mrs. Moake buys one hundred balloons for her grandchildren. She wants to divide the balloons equally among her ten grandchildren. How many balloons will she give to each grandchild?

T: _____

I: _____

_____

N: _____

S: _____

_____

WORK SPACE

**15.** Twelve monkeys climb a banana tree. Each monkey eats five bananas. How many bananas do the monkeys eat in all?

T: _____

I: _____

_____

N: _____

S: _____

_____

WORK SPACE

**16.** Mr. Bradley plans to divide $20 among his 4 children. He wants to give each of them an equal amount of money. How much will each child receive?

T: _____

I: _____

_____

N: _____

S: _____

_____

WORK SPACE

**17.** After the school supplies have been given out, the principal of Pine Valley Elementary School finds sixty-four more bottles of glue. She separates the bottles and puts an equal number into eight different boxes. How many bottles of glue are in each box?

T: _____

I: _____

_____

N: _____

S: _____

_____

WORK SPACE

**18.** Four friends each save $10 to spend on a field trip. How much money do they save altogether?

T: _____

I: _____

_____

N: _____

S: _____

_____

WORK SPACE

**19.** At a furniture store, 11 chairs are on sale. Each chair has 4 legs. How many chair legs are there in all?

T: _____

I: _____

_____

N: _____

S: _____

_____

WORK SPACE

**20.** Tamara used to keep her stamp collection in a shoebox. Now she wants to move her 80 stamps to an album. Tamara's album has 20 pages, and she would like to place the same number of stamps on each page. How many stamps should she put on each page?

T: _____

I: _____

_____

N: _____

S: _____

_____

WORK SPACE

# Final Mixed Review

Use **TINS** to solve these problems.

---

**1.** Maggie needs to wash two baskets of laundry. Each basket contains twenty dirty items. How many items will be washed in all?

Thought: _____

Information: _____

_____

Number Sentence: _____

Solution Sentence: _____

_____

WORK SPACE

---

**2.** Juan Carlo has $39. Jennifer has $21. How much more money does Juan Carlo have than Jennifer?

T: _____

I: _____

_____

N: _____

S: _____

_____

WORK SPACE

**3.** Teronia plants five rows of pansies in her garden. Each row has eight pansies in it. What is the total number of pansies Teronia plants?

T: _____

I: _____

_____

N: _____

S: _____

_____

WORK SPACE

**4.** Yanira needs to write a twelve-page report for her history class. She decides to write an equal number of pages each day for three days. How many pages will Yanira write each day?

T: _____

I: _____

_____

N: _____

S: _____

_____

WORK SPACE

**5.** Matthew studied for 2 hours on Monday, 3 hours on Tuesday, and 3 hours on Wednesday. He also spent 2 hours at karate practice on Wednesday. What is the total number of hours Matthew spent studying during the 3 days?

T: _____

I: _____

_____

N: _____

S: _____

_____

WORK SPACE

**6.** Johnny has 43 pictures of airplanes. His uncle gives him 2 magazines, and Johnny finds 11 more pictures of planes. How many pictures of airplanes does Johnny have altogether?

T: _____

I: _____

_____

N: _____

S: _____

_____

WORK SPACE

**7.** Eddie earns $7 each week for his allowance. His dad subtracted $3 from this week's allowance because Eddie forgot to make his bed 3 times. How much money did Eddie earn this week?

T: _____

I: _____

_____

N: _____

S: _____

_____

WORK SPACE

**8.** Martina and Louis are on a ten-hour train ride. They sleep for the first six hours of the trip. How much time do they have left on the train?

T: _____

I: _____

_____

N: _____

S: _____

_____

WORK SPACE

**9.** Miranda's bedroom has two windows. She tapes twelve paper snowflakes to each window. How many paper snowflakes are there in all?

T: _____

I: _____

_____

N: _____

S: _____

_____

WORK SPACE

**10.** The gym teacher needs to put away twenty-one softballs. She stores an equal number of softballs in three different boxes. How many softballs does she store in each box?

T: _____

I: _____

_____

N: _____

S: _____

_____

WORK SPACE

**11.** On the playground there are 6 buckets filled with jump ropes. Each bucket has 11 jump ropes in it. How many jump ropes are there altogether?

T: _____

I: _____

_____

N: _____

S: _____

_____

WORK SPACE

**12.** Sandy baby-sat his younger cousins for five hours on Friday, three hours on Saturday, and three hours on Sunday. How many total hours did Sandy baby-sit on Saturday and Sunday?

T: _____

I: _____

_____

N: _____

S: _____

_____

WORK SPACE

**13.** Thad and Teresita are in charge of washing the family dishes. During one week they washed 46 plates, 34 glasses, and 33 bowls. How many plates and bowls did Thad and Teresita wash in all?

WORK SPACE

T: _____

I: _____

_____

N: _____

S: _____

_____

**14.** Cassandra and James collect rocks. One afternoon they find 18 unusual rocks. They decide to divide the rocks evenly between them. How many rocks does each child keep?

WORK SPACE

T: _____

I: _____

_____

N: _____

S: _____

_____

**15.** Renee bounced a basketball 43 times in a row. Miguel bounced the ball 38 times in a row. What is the difference in the number of times Renee and Miguel bounced the basketball?

T: _____

I: _____

_____

N: _____

S: _____

_____

WORK SPACE

**16.** Ms. Jones has twenty-five rubber bands. She separates them into five equal piles. How many rubber bands are in each pile?

T: _____

I: _____

_____

N: _____

S: _____

_____

WORK SPACE

**21.** Create your own word problem. It can be an addition, subtraction, multiplication, or division problem. Next use TINS to solve the problem. Then write at least 2 sentences explaining how you solved the problem.

Question: _____

_____

_____

_____

T: _____

I: _____

_____

N: _____

S: _____

_____

Explanation: _____

_____

_____

_____

WORK SPACE

**22.** Create another word problem. You may want to include extra information to make the problem tricky. Next use TINS to solve the problem. Then write at least 2 sentences explaining how you solved the problem.

Question: _____

_____

_____

_____

T: _____

I: _____

_____

N: _____

S: _____

_____

Explanation: _____

_____

_____

_____

WORK SPACE

You can write the key words that you know in each operation sign. Then cut out the signs and put them on your desk or in your math folder.

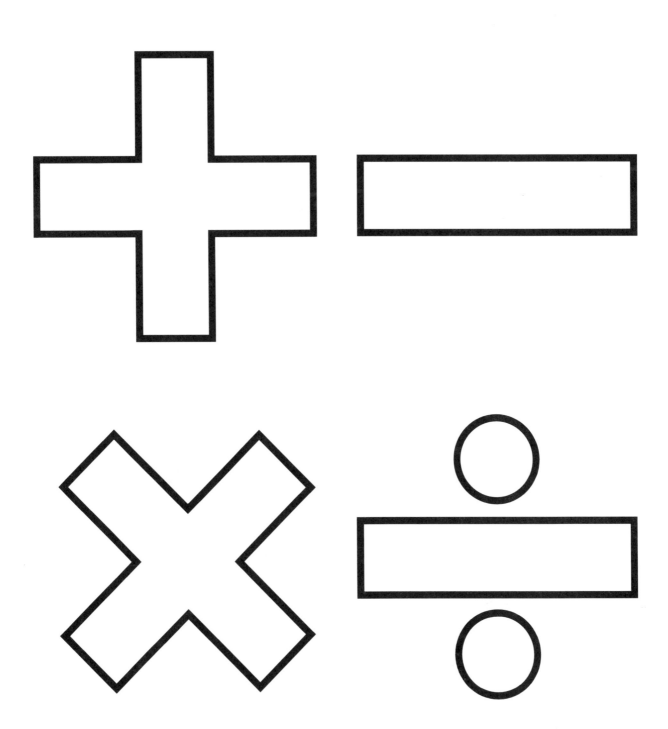